Chemistry for the Grammar Stage

Student Workbook

Chemistry for the Grammar Stage Student Workbook

Third Edition (First Printing)
Copyright @ Elemental Science, Inc.
Email: support@elementalscience.com

ISBN # 978-1-953490-17-9

Printed in the USA for worldwide distribution

For more copies write to:
Elemental Science
PO Box 79
Niceville, FL 32588
support@elementalscience.com

Copyright Policy

Classical SCIENCE

A Quick Welcome from the Author

Dear Student,

Welcome to chemistry! This workbook will serve as a scrapbook of sorts for you to share what you have learned about the principles of chemistry. You will be learning about atoms, the periodic table, and so much more.

Each week you and your teacher will do the following:

- ☞ **Read** the assigned pages together. Your teacher will then ask you a few questions as you discuss what was read. Be sure to share what you found interesting.

- ☞ **Do** the weekly demonstration with your teacher. This is the super fun part of science, plus you get to exercise your observation muscles. Be sure to pay close attention and help out when your teachers ask you to do so.

- ☞ **Write** down what you have learned and seen. Your teacher may help you with the actual writing, but be sure to record the facts that you want to remember.

Your teacher has the tools to add in more each week, things like memory work, library books, and extra activities. Be sure to let them know if you want to dig deeper into a topic.

And, if you have a question or want to share your work with me, please have your teacher send us an email (support@elementalscience.com) or tag us (@elementalscience) in a photo you share online. I would love to see what you have learned!

I hope that you enjoy learning about chemistry this year!

Paige Hudson

Table of Contents

A Peek Inside Your Student Workbook

1. Weekly Notebooking Pages

Here is your chance to share what you found interesting about what you read about each week. Each of these customized notebooking pages have space for you (or your teacher) to write, along with a simple black-line illustration for you to color.

2. Simple Demonstration Sheets

These pages allow you to document the hands-on scientific demonstrations you do with your teacher. There are sections for your materials, your method, your outcome, and your insights, or thoughts, from the demonstration.

3. Glossary of Terms

You can keep a glossary of words that you covered this year as part of your student workbook. These words are listed in alphabetical order with pictures to help you remember the vocabulary.

4. Memory Worksheets

You can work on the memory work with the poster-style sheets found after the glossary. Each poem has illustrations you can color that will help you remember the information in the poem.

5. Review Sheets

Finally, you will see review sheets at the back of this workbook. These may or may not be assigned by your teacher.

And now that you know what is in your workbook, let's dig in!

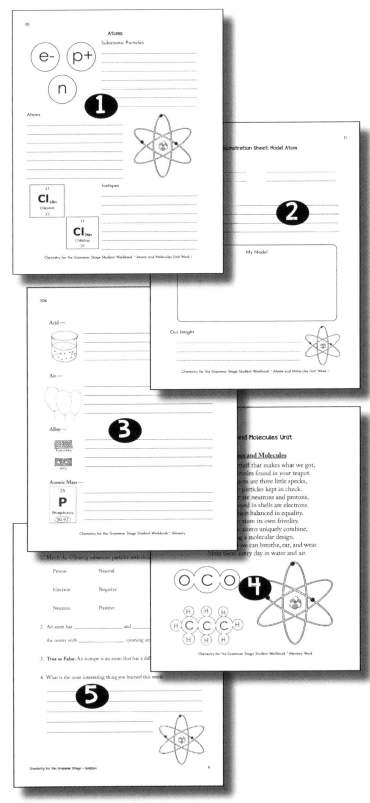

Chemistry for the Grammar Stage Teacher Guide ~ At-a-glance

Chemistry for the Grammar Stage

Atoms and Molecules Unit

Atoms and Molecules Poster

Subatomic Particles

Atoms and Elements

Molecules and Compounds

Atoms

Subatomic Particles

e- p+ n

_____
_____
_____
_____
_____
_____
_____

Atoms

_____
_____
_____
_____
_____
_____
_____

| 17 |
| **Cl** 18n |
| Chlorine |
| 35 |

| 17 |
| **Cl** 20n |
| Chlorine |
| 37 |

Isotopes

_____
_____
_____
_____
_____
_____

Demonstration Sheet: Model Atom

Our Tools

_____   _____

_____   _____

Our Method

_____

_____

_____

_____

Our Outcome

My Model

Our Insight

_____

_____

_____

Chemistry for the Grammar Stage Student Workbook ~ Atoms and Molecules Unit Week 1

12

Molecules

Electron Shells

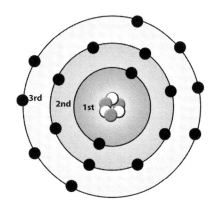

_____ electrons fit in the first shell.

_____ electrons fit in the second shell.

_____ electrons fit in the third shell.

Molecules

_____

_____

_____

_____

_____

_____

_____

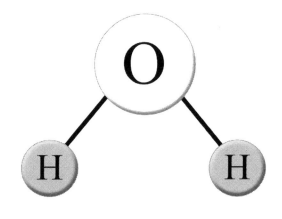

Polar and Nonpolar

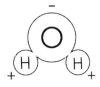

_____

_____

_____

_____

_____

_____

_____

Demonstration Sheet: Moving Molecules

Our Tools

_____   _____

_____   _____

_____   _____

Our Method

_____

_____

_____

Our Outcome

First Observation	After 1 Hour

Air

_____

_____

_____

_____

_____

_____

_____

_____

_____

_____

_____

_____

_____

_____

_____

_____

_____

_____

_____

_____

Demonstration Sheet: Fresh Air

Our Tools

_____   _____

_____   _____

Our Method

What it looked like

_____

_____

_____

_____

_____

_____

_____

_____

_____

_____

Our Outcome

_____

_____

_____

_____

Our Insight

_____

_____

_____

Water

_____
_____
_____
_____
_____
_____
_____
_____
_____
_____
_____
_____
_____
_____

3. Water vapor condenses to form clouds.

2. The water rises into the air as water vapor.

4. Water vapor cools, the clouds become heavy, and water falls as rain.

1. The Sun's heat evaporates water from the world's oceans, lakes, and rivers.

5. Rainwater flows back into the rivers, lakes, and oceans.

Demonstration Sheet: Disappearing Salt

Our Tools

_____   _____

_____   _____

Our Method

What it looked like

_____

_____

_____

_____

_____

_____

_____

_____

_____

Our Outcome

_____

_____

_____

_____

Our Insight

_____

_____

_____

Chemistry for the Grammar Stage

Periodic Table Unit

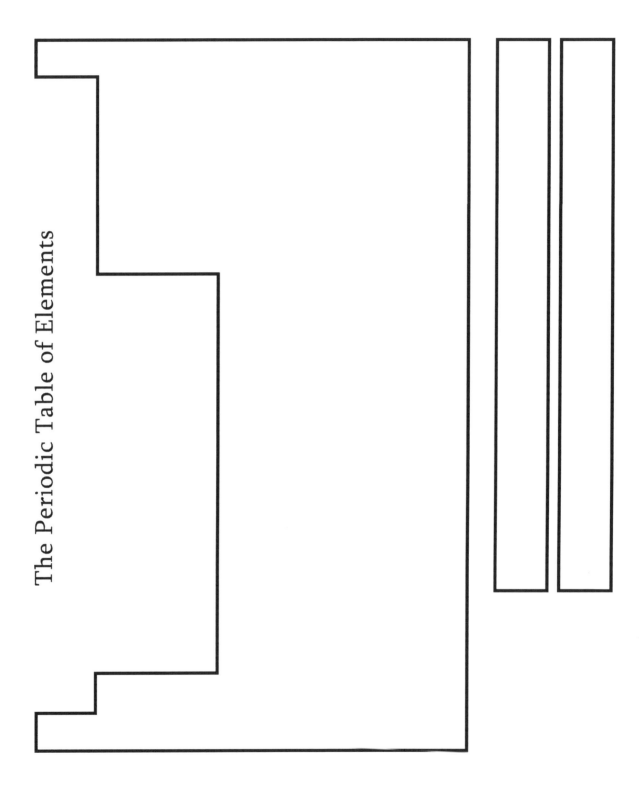

The Periodic Table of Elements

The Periodic Table of Elements

15
P
Phosphorus
30.97

Elements

_____

_____

_____

_____

_____

_____

_____

_____

_____

Periodic Table

_____

_____

_____

_____

_____

_____

_____

_____

_____

1 H Hydrogen 1.008																	2 He Helium 4.003
3 Li Lithium 6.941	4 Be Beryllium 9.012											5 B Boron 10.81	6 C Carbon 12.01	7 N Nitrogen 14.01	8 O Oxygen 16.00	9 F Fluorine 19.00	10 Ne Neon 20.18
11 Na Sodium 22.99	12 Mg Magnesium 24.31											13 Al Aluminum 26.98	14 Si Silicon 28.09	15 P Phosphorus 30.97	16 S Sulfur 32.07	17 Cl Chlorine 35.45	18 Ar Argon 39.95
19 K 39.10	20 Ca 40.08	21 Sc 44.96	22 Ti 47.87	23 V 50.94	24 Cr 52.00	25 Mn 54.94	26 Fe 55.85	27 Co 58.93	28 Ni 58.69	29 Cu 63.55	30 Zn 65.39	31 Ga 69.72	32 Ge 72.61	33 As 74.92	34 Se 78.96	35 Br 79.90	36 Kr 83.80
37 Rb 85.47	38 Sr 87.62	39 Y 88.91	40 Zr 91.22	41 Nb 92.91	42 Mo 95.94	43 Tc 98.91	44 Ru 101.1	45 Rh 102.9	46 Pd 106.4	47 Ag 107.9	48 Cd 112.4	49 In 114.8	50 Sn 118.7	51 Sb 121.8	52 Te 127.6	53 I 126.9	54 Xe 131.3
55 Cs 132.9	56 Ba 137.3	* 71 Lu 175.0	72 Hf 178.5	73 Ta 181.0	74 W 183.9	75 Re 186.2	76 Os 190.2	77 Ir 192.2	78 Pt 195.1	79 Au 197.0	80 Hg 200.6	81 Tl 204.4	82 Pb 207.2	83 Bi 209.0	84 Po [209]	85 At [210]	86 Rn [222]
87 Fr [223]	88 Ra [226]	** 103 Lr [262]	104 Rf [261]	105 Db [262]	106 Sg [266]	107 Bh [264]	108 Hs [269]	109 Mt [268]	110 Ds [272]	111 Rg [272]	112 Cn [285]	113 Nh [286]	114 Fl [289]	115 Mc [289]	116 Lv [293]	117 Ts [294]	118 Og [294]

*Lanthanides

57 La 138.9	58 Ce 140.1	59 Pr 140.9	60 Nd 144.2	61 Pm [145]	62 Sm 150.4	63 Eu 152.0	64 Gd 157.3	65 Tb 158.9	66 Dy 162.5	67 Ho 164.9	68 Er 167.3	69 Tm 168.9	70 Yb 173.0

**Actinides

89 Ac [227]	90 Th 232.0	91 Pa 231.0	92 U 238.0	93 Np [237]	94 Pu [244]	95 Am [243]	96 Cm [247]	97 Bk [247]	98 Cf [251]	99 Es [252]	100 Fm [257]	101 Md [258]	102 No [259]

Demonstration Sheet: Table Sorting

Our Tools

_____   _____

_____   _____

Our Outcome

My Table

Our Insight

_____

_____

_____

Chemistry for the Grammar Stage Student Workbook ~ Periodic Table Unit Week 1

1
H
Hydrogen
1.008

3
Li
Lithium
6.941

11
Na
Sodium
22.99

19
K
Potassium
39.10

37
Rb
Rubidium
85.47

55
Cs
Cesium
132.9

87
Fr
Francium
[223]

Alkali Metals

_____

_____

_____

_____

_____

_____

_____

_____

_____

_____

_____

_____

_____

_____

_____

_____

_____

_____

Demonstration Sheet: Which one freezes first?

Our Tools

_____   _____

_____   _____

_____   _____

Our Method

_____

_____

_____

_____

Our Outcome

Time	Temperature Cup #1	Temperature Cup #2	Temperature Cup #3
0 Minutes			
30 Minutes			
60 Minutes			
90 Minutes			
120 Minutes			

Our Insight

_____

_____

_____

| 11 |
| **Na** |
| Sodium |
| 22.99 |

4
Be
Beryllium
9.012

12
Mg
Magnesium
24.31

20
Ca
Calcium
40.08

38
Sr
Strontium
87.62

56
Ba
Barium
137.3

88
Ra
Radium
[226]

Alkaline Earth Metals

Demonstration Sheet: Magnesium Solutions

Our Tools

_____   _____

_____   _____

_____   _____

Our Method

What it looked like

_____

_____

_____

_____

_____

_____

_____

_____

_____

_____

Our Outcome

_____

_____

_____

_____

Our Insight

| 12 |
| Mg |
| Magnesium |
| 24.31 |

_____

_____

_____

28

Transition Metals

_____
_____
_____
_____
_____
_____
_____
_____
_____
_____
_____
_____
_____

21	22	23	24	25	26	27	28	29	30
Sc	**Ti**	**V**	**Cr**	**Mn**	**Fe**	**Co**	**Ni**	**Cu**	**Zn**
Scandium	Titanium	Vanadium	Chromium	Manganese	Iron	Cobalt	Nickel	Copper	Zinc
44.96	47.87	50.94	52.00	54.94	55.85	58.93	58.69	63.55	65.39
39	40	41	42	43	44	45	46	47	48
Y	**Zr**	**Nb**	**Mo**	**Tc**	**Ru**	**Rh**	**Pd**	**Ag**	**Cd**
Yttrium	Zirconium	Niobium	Molybdenum	Technetium	Ruthenium	Rhodium	Palladium	Silver	Cadmium
88.91	91.22	92.91	95.94	98.91	101.1	102.9	106.4	107.9	112.4
* 71	72	73	74	75	76	77	78	79	80
Lu	**Hf**	**Ta**	**W**	**Re**	**Os**	**Ir**	**Pt**	**Au**	**Hg**
Lutetium	Hafnium	Tantalum	Tungsten	Rhenium	Osmium	Iridium	Platinum	Gold	Mercury
175.0	178.5	181.0	183.9	186.2	190.2	192.2	195.1	197.0	200.6

Chemistry for the Grammar Stage Student Workbook ~ Periodic Table Unit Week 4

Demonstration Sheet: Rusted

Our Tools

_____   _____

_____   _____

Our Method

_____

_____

_____

_____

_____

Our Outcome

At the start	At the end

Our Insight

_____

_____

_____

_____

26
Fe
Iron
55.85

5
B
Boron
10.81
13
Al
Aluminum
26.98
31
Ga
Gallium
69.72
49
In
Indium
114.8
81
Tl
Thallium
204.4
113
Nh
Nihonium
[286]

Boron Elements

_____
_____
_____
_____
_____
_____
_____
_____
_____
_____
_____
_____
_____
_____
_____
_____
_____

Demonstration Sheet: Aluminum Gel

Our Tools

_____   _____

_____   _____

_____   _____

Our Method

┌─────────────────────────┐
│ What it looked like   │   _____
│   │   _____
│   │   _____
│   │   _____
│   │   _____
│   │   _____
│   │   _____
│   │   _____
│   │   _____
└─────────────────────────┘   _____

Our Outcome

_____

_____

_____

_____

Our Insight

| 13 |
| **Al** |
| Aluminum |
| 26.98 |

_____

_____

_____

6
C
Carbon
12.01

14
Si
Silicon
28.09

32
Ge
Germanium
72.61

50
Sn
Tin
118.71

82
Pb
Lead
207.2

114
Fl
Flerovium

Carbon Elements

Demonstration Sheet: Carbon Towers

Our Tools

_____   _____

_____   _____

_____   _____

Our Method

What it looked like

_____
_____
_____
_____
_____
_____
_____
_____
_____

Our Outcome

_____

_____

_____

_____

Our Insight

_____

_____

_____

6
C
Carbon
12.01

7
N
Nitrogen
14.01
15
P
Phosphorus
30.97
33
As
Arsenic
74.92
51
Sb
Antimony
121.8
83
Bi
Bismuth
209.0
115
Mc
Moscovium
[289]

Nitrogen Elements

_____

_____

_____

_____

_____

_____

_____

_____

_____

_____

_____

_____

_____

_____

_____

_____

_____

_____

_____

Demonstration Sheet: Shiny Pennies

Our Tools

_____   _____

_____   _____

_____   _____

Our Method

_____

_____

_____

_____

Our Outcome

Before	After

Our Insight

_____

_____

_____

_____

15
P
Phosphorus
30.97

8
O
Oxygen
16.00

16
S
Sulfur
32.07

34
Se
Selenium
78.96

52
Te
Tellurium
127.6

84
Po
Polonium
[209]

116
Lv
Livermorium
[293]

Oxygen Elements

Demonstration Sheet: Breathing Flame

Our Tools

_____   _____

_____   _____

_____   _____

Our Method

_____

_____

_____

_____

Our Outcome

Uncovered	Covered with a Jar

Our Insight

_____

_____

_____

_____

8

O

Oxygen
16.00

9
F
Fluorine
19.00
17
Cl
Chlorine
35.45
35
Br
Bromine
79.90
53
I
Iodine
126.9
85
At
Astatine
[210]
117
Ts
Tennessine
[294]

Halogens

_____
_____
_____
_____
_____
_____
_____
_____
_____
_____
_____
_____
_____
_____
_____
_____
_____
_____
_____
_____
_____
_____

Demonstration Sheet: Iodine Testing

Our Tools

_____   _____

_____   _____

_____   _____

Our Method

_____

_____

_____

_____

Our Outcome

Sample	Observations
Potato	
Bread	
Fruit	

Our Insight

_____

_____

_____

_____

53
I
Iodine
126.9

2
He
Helium
4.003

10
Ne
Neon
20.18

18
Ar
Argon
39.95

36
Kr
Krypton
83.80

54
Xe
Xenon
131.3

86
Rn
Radon
[222]

118
Og
Oganesson
[294]

Noble Gases

_____

_____

_____

_____

_____

_____

_____

_____

_____

_____

_____

_____

_____

_____

_____

_____

_____

_____

_____

_____

Demonstration Sheet: Funny Voice

Our Tools

_____   _____

_____   _____

_____   _____

Our Method

_____

_____

_____

_____

_____

Our Outcome

_____

_____

_____

_____

_____

Our Insight

_____

_____

_____

_____

| 2 |
| **He** |
| Helium |
| 4.003 |

Lanthanides

_____
_____
_____
_____
_____
_____
_____
_____
_____
_____
_____
_____
_____
_____
_____
_____
_____
_____
_____
_____

57	58	59	60	61	62	63	64	65	66	67	68	69	70
La	**Ce**	**Pr**	**Nd**	**Pm**	**Sm**	**Eu**	**Gd**	**Tb**	**Dy**	**Ho**	**Er**	**Tm**	**Yb**
Lanthanum	Cerium	Praseodymium	Neodymium	Promethium	Samarium	Europium	Gadolinium	Terbium	Dysprosium	Holmium	Erbium	Thulium	Ytterbium
138.9	140.1	140.9	144.2	[145]	150.4	152.0	157.3	158.9	162.5	164.9	167.3	168.9	173.0

Demonstration Sheet: Moving Pencils

Our Tools

_____   _____

_____   _____

_____   _____

Our Method

_____

_____

_____

_____

Our Outcome

What it looked like

Our Insight

_____

_____

_____

| 57 |
| **La** |
| Lanthanum |
| 138.9 |

Actindes

_____

_____

_____

_____

_____

_____

_____

_____

_____

_____

_____

_____

_____

_____

_____

_____

_____

_____

_____

89	90	91	92	93	94	95	96	97	98	99	100	101	102
Ac	**Th**	**Pa**	**U**	**Np**	**Pu**	**Am**	**Cm**	**Bk**	**Cf**	**Es**	**Fm**	**Md**	**No**
Actinium	Thorium	Protactinium	Uranium	Neptunium	Plutonium	Americium	Curium	Berkelium	Californium	Einsteinium	Fermium	Mendelevium	Nobelium
[227]	232.0	231.0	238.0	[237]	[244]	[243]	[247]	[247]	[251]	[252]	[257]	[258]	[259]

Demonstration Sheet: Half-life

Our Tools

_____   _____

_____   _____

_____   _____

Our Method

_____

_____

_____

_____

_____

Our Outcome

_____

_____

_____

_____

_____

Our Insight

_____

_____

_____

_____

_____

89
Ac
Actinium
[227]

Chemistry for the Grammar Stage

Physical Changes Unit

States of Matter Poster

Gases

Liquids

Solids

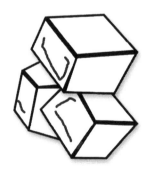

States of Matter

_____

_____

_____

_____

_____

_____

_____

_____

_____

_____

_____

_____

_____

_____

_____

_____

_____

_____

_____

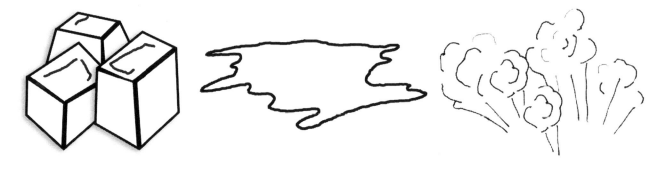

Chemistry for the Grammar Stage Student Workbook ~ Physical Changes Unit Week 1

Demonstration Sheet: Playing with Matter

Our Tools

_____   _____

_____   _____

Our Method

_____

_____

_____

_____

Our Outcome

	My Observations
Balloon with Ice	
Balloon with Water	
Balloon with Air	

Our Insight

_____

_____

_____

Changes in State

Melting

Freezing

Boiling

Condensing

Demonstration Sheet: Freezy Meltdown

Our Tools

_____   _____

_____   _____

Our Method

_____

_____

_____

_____

Our Outcome

	My Observations
Juice (At the beginning)	
Juice (After time in freezer)	
Juice (After time on the counter)	

Our Insight

_____

_____

_____

Solid
Liquid
Gas

Liquid Behavior

_____

_____

_____

_____

_____

_____

_____

_____

_____

_____

_____

_____

_____

_____

_____

_____

_____

Demonstration Sheet: Liquid Surface

Our Tools

_____   _____

_____   _____

Our Method

_____

_____

_____

_____

Our Outcome

What it looked like

Our Insight

_____

_____

_____

_____

Chemistry for the Grammar Stage Student Workbook ~ Physical Changes Unit Week 3

Gas Behavior

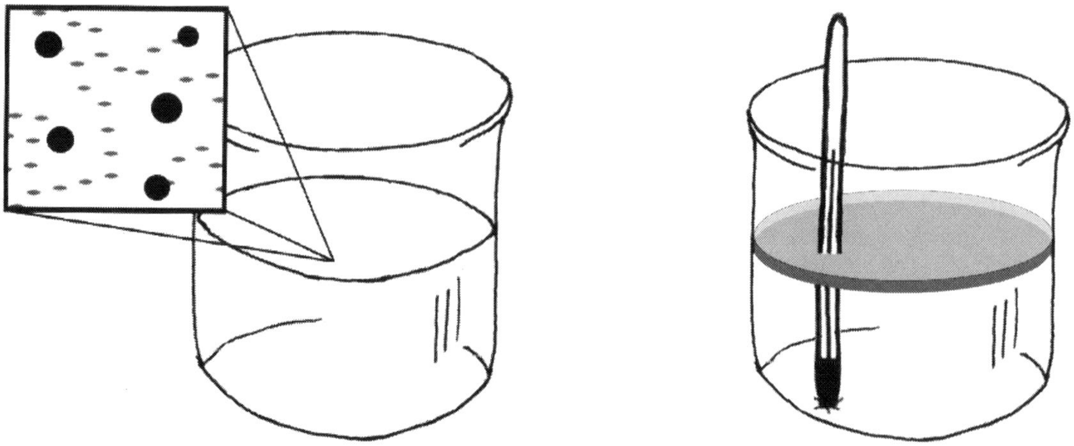

Demonstration Sheet: Can Crusher

Our Tools

_____   _____

_____   _____

Our Method

┌─────────────────────────────┐
| What it looked like | _____
| | _____
| | _____
| | _____
| | _____
| | _____
| | _____
| | _____
| | _____
| | _____
└─────────────────────────────┘   _____

Our Outcome

_____

_____

_____

Our Insight

_____

_____

_____

_____

Chemistry for the Grammar Stage

Chemical Changes Unit

60

Chemical Changes Poster

Ionic Bonding

Covalent bonding

Metallic bonding

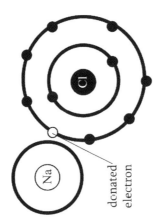

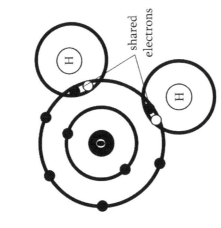

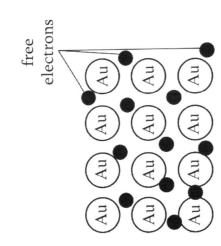

$$HCl + NaOH \rightarrow H_2O + NaCl$$

Exothermic / Endothermic

Oxidation / Reduction

Chemistry for the Grammar Stage Student Workbook ~ Chemical Changes Unit Project

Bonding

_____

_____

_____

_____

_____

_____

_____

_____

_____

_____

_____

_____

_____

_____

_____

_____

_____

donated electron

shared electrons

Demonstration Sheet: Bond Breaking

Our Tools

_____   _____

_____   _____

Our Method

_____

_____

_____

_____

_____

Our Outcome

What it looked like (salt alone)	What it looked like (salt and water)

Our Insight

additional electron

Cl-

_____

_____

_____

Chemical Reactions

_____

_____

_____

_____

_____

_____

_____

_____

_____

_____

_____

_____

_____

_____

_____

_____

_____

_____

_____

$$HCl + NaOH \longrightarrow H_2O + NaCl$$

Demonstration Sheet: Penny Change

Our Tools

_____   _____

_____   _____

Our Method

_____

_____

_____

_____

Our Outcome

What it looked like

_____

_____

_____

_____

_____

_____

_____

_____

_____

Our Insight

_____

_____

_____

_____

66

Types of Reactions

_____
_____
_____
_____
_____
_____
_____
_____
_____
_____
_____
_____
_____
_____
_____
_____
_____
_____
_____
_____
_____
_____
_____

Demonstration Sheet: Types of Reaction

Our Tools

_____   _____

_____   _____

Our Method

_____

_____

_____

_____

_____

Our Outcome

	What happened to the temperature of the cup?	Type of Reaction
Baking Soda + Vinegar		
Epsom Salts + Water		

Our Insight

_____

_____

_____

_____

Oxidation and Reduction

_____

_____

_____

_____

_____

_____

_____

_____

_____

_____

_____

_____

_____

_____

_____

Demonstration Sheet: Browning

Our Tools

_____   _____

_____   _____

Our Method

_____

_____

_____

_____

_____

Our Outcome

Time	Plain Apple Half	Apple Half with Lemon Juice
After 1 hour		
After 2 hours		
After 3 hours		
After 4 hours		

Our Insight

_____

_____

_____

_____

Chemistry for the Grammar Stage

Mixtures Unit

Mixture Poster

Separating Mixtures

Filtration   Chromatography   Distillation

Crystals

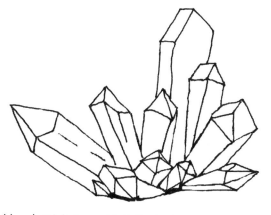

Mixtures

_____
_____
_____
_____
_____
_____
_____
_____
_____
_____
_____
_____
_____
_____
_____
_____
_____
_____

Demonstration Sheet: Disappearing Powder

Our Tools

_____   _____

_____   _____

Our Method

┌─────────────────────────────┐ _____
│   What it looked like   │ _____
│   │ _____
│   │ _____
│   │ _____
│   │ _____
│   │ _____
│   │ _____
│   │ _____
└─────────────────────────────┘ _____

Our Outcome

_____

_____

_____

_____

Our Insight

_____

_____

_____

_____

76

Separating Mixtures

_____
_____
_____
_____
_____
_____
_____
_____
_____
_____
_____
_____
_____
_____
_____
_____
_____
_____

Demonstration Sheet: Separating Colors

Our Tools

_____   _____

_____   _____

Our Method

_____

_____

_____

_____

Our Outcome

What it looked like

Our Insight

_____

_____

_____

_____

Chemistry for the Grammar Stage Student Workbook ~ Mixtures Unit Week 2

78

Crystals

_____

_____

_____

_____

_____

_____

_____

_____

_____

_____

_____

_____

_____

_____

_____

_____

_____

_____

_____

_____

_____

Demonstration Sheet: Crystalline Shapes

Our Tools

_____   _____

_____   _____

Our Method

_____

_____

_____

_____

Our Outcome

What it looked like

Our Insight

_____

_____

_____

_____

Scientist Biography Questionnaire – Louis Pasteur

Title of Book

_____

When and where was Louis Pasteur born?

_____

_____

What was his major scientific contribution?

_____

_____

_____

_____

_____

List the events that surround his discovery.

_____

_____

_____

_____

_____

_____

_____

_____

_____

_____

_____

_____

List some other interesting events in the his life.

_____

_____

_____

_____

_____

_____

_____

_____

_____

_____

_____

_____

Why do you think that it is important to learn about Louis Pasteur?

_____

_____

_____

_____

_____

_____

_____

_____

Chemistry for the Grammar Stage

Acids and Bases Unit

Acids

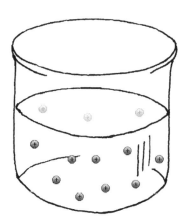

Bases

Acids and Bases, Part 1

Acids

_____

_____

_____

_____

_____

_____

_____

_____

_____

_____

_____

Bases

_____

_____

_____

_____

_____

_____

_____

_____

_____

_____

Demonstration Sheet: Kitchen Acid

Our Tools

_____   _____

_____   _____

Our Method

_____

_____

_____

_____

Our Outcome

	Color of solution
Cabbage Juice Only	
Cabbage Juice + Water	
Cabbage Juice + Water + Lemon Juice	

Our Insight

_____

_____

_____

_____

88

Acids and Bases, Part 2

_____

_____

_____

_____

_____

_____

_____

_____

_____

14
13
12
11
10
9
8

Basic Range

7 ——————————— Neutral

6
5
4
3
2
1
0

Acidic Range

Demonstration Sheet: Testing Strips

Our Tools

_____   _____

_____   _____

Our Method

_____

_____

_____

_____

Our Outcome

	Cabbage Paper Strip
Vinegar	
Ammonia	

_____

_____

_____

Our Insight

_____

_____

_____

Neutral

Base   Acid

Neutralization

Base + Acid

Demonstration Sheet: Neutralize It

Our Tools

_____   _____

_____   _____

Our Method

_____

_____

_____

_____

Our Outcome

What it looked like at the end

_____

_____

_____

_____

_____

_____

_____

_____

Our Insight

_____

_____

_____

_____

Base + Acid

Scientist Biography Questionnaire – Marie Curie

Title of Book

_____

When and where was Marie Curie born?

_____

_____

What was her major scientific contribution?

_____

_____

_____

_____

List the events that surround her discovery.

_____

_____

_____

_____

_____

_____

_____

_____

_____

_____

_____

List some other interesting events in the her life.

_____

_____

_____

_____

_____

_____

_____

_____

_____

_____

_____

Why do you think that it is important to learn about Marie Curie?

_____

_____

_____

_____

_____

_____

_____

Chemistry for the Grammar Stage

Organic Chemistry Unit

Organic Compounds

_____
_____
_____
_____
_____
_____
_____
_____
_____
_____
_____
_____
_____

_____
_____
_____
_____
_____
_____
_____
_____

Demonstration Sheet: Fat Test

Our Tools

_____   _____

_____   _____

Our Method

_____

_____

_____

_____

_____

Our Outcome

Type of Food: Did it leave a stain? yes no	Type of Food: Did it leave a stain? yes no	Type of Food: Did it leave a stain? yes no
Type of Food: Did it leave a stain? yes no	Type of Food: Did it leave a stain? yes no	Type of Food: Did it leave a stain? yes no

Our Insight

_____

_____

_____

Alcohols and Detergents

Alcohols

Detergents

Esters

Demonstration Sheet: Scented Alcohol

Our Tools

_____   _____

_____   _____

Our Method

_____

_____

_____

_____

_____

Our Outcome

_____

_____

_____

_____

_____

Our Insight

_____

_____

_____

_____

_____

_____

Hydrocarbons

_____
_____
_____
_____
_____
_____
_____
_____
_____
_____
_____
_____
_____
_____
_____
_____
_____
_____
_____
_____
_____
_____
_____
_____

Demonstration Sheet: Oily Clean-up

Our Tools

_____   _____

_____   _____

_____   _____

Our Method

_____

_____

_____

_____

Our Outcome

Material	How well did the material clean up the oil?
Spoon	
Cotton balls	
Polyester felt	

Our Insight

_____

_____

_____

Polymers and Plastics

Polymers

_____
_____
_____
_____
_____
_____
_____
_____
_____
_____
_____

Plastics

_____
_____
_____
_____
_____
_____
_____
_____
_____
_____

Demonstration Sheet: Kitchen Plastic

Our Tools

_____   _____

_____   _____

Our Method

What it looked like

Our Outcome

_____

_____

_____

Our Insight

_____

_____

_____

_____

Chemistry for the Grammar Stage

Glossary

Acid —

_____
_____
_____
_____

Air —

_____
_____
_____
_____

Alloy —

Pure Metal

_____
_____

Alloy

_____
_____

Atomic Mass —

15

P

Phosphorus

30.97

_____
_____
_____
_____

Atomic Number —

15
P
Phosphorus
30.97

_____

_____

_____

_____

Base —

_____

_____

_____

_____

Catalyst —

Reaction Pathway

normal
path of a
reaction

activation
energy

activation energy
when a catalyst has
been introduced

reaction path
with the
addition of a
catalyst

reactants

products

_____

_____

_____

Chemical Bond —

O

H

H

shared
electrons

_____

_____

_____

_____

Chemical Reaction —

$HCl + NaOH \longrightarrow H_2O + NaCl$

_____

_____

_____

_____

Chemical Symbol —

15
P
Phosphorus
30.97

_____

_____

_____

_____

Chromatography —

_____

_____

_____

_____

Crystal —

_____

_____

_____

_____

Detergent —

_____
_____
_____
_____

Diffusion —

Open Valve

_____
_____
_____
_____

Electron —

e-

_____
_____
_____
_____

Electron Shell —

3rd 2nd 1st

_____
_____
_____
_____

Element —

13
Al
Aluminum
26.98

_____
_____
_____
_____

Enzyme —

_____
_____
_____
_____

Essential Element —

6
C
Carbon
12.01

_____
_____
_____
_____

Evaporation —

_____
_____
_____
_____

Fermentation —

_____
_____
_____
_____

Hard Water —

_____
_____
_____
_____

Indicator —

_____
_____
_____
_____

Inert —

_____
_____
_____
_____

Ion —

H+

Isotope —

Cl_{18n}
Chlorine
35
17

Cl_{20n}
Chlorine
37
17

Metal —

13
Al
Aluminum
26.98

31
Ga
Gallium
69.72

49
In
Indium
114.8

50
Sn
Tin
118.7

81
Tl
Thallium
204.4

82
Pb
Lead
207.2

83
Bi
Bismuth
209.0

Metalloid —

5
B
Boron
10.81

14
Si
Silicon
28.09

32
Ge
Germanium
72.61

33
As
Arsenic
74.92

51
Sb
Antimony
121.8

52
Te
Tellurium
127.6

84
Po
Polonium
[209]

Mixture —

_____
_____
_____
_____

Molecule —

_____
_____
_____
_____

Neutralization —

Base   Acid

_____
_____
_____
_____

Neutron —

n

_____
_____
_____
_____

Nonmetal —

6	7	8
C Carbon 12.01	**N** Nitrogen 14.01	**O** Oxygen 16
	15 **P** Phosphorus 30.97	16 **S** Sulfur 32.07
		34 **Se** Selenium 78.96

_____

_____

_____

_____

Organic Compound —

_____

_____

_____

_____

Oxidation —

_____

_____

_____

_____

Periodic Table —

_____

_____

_____

_____

pH —

Physical Change —

Polymer —

Proton —

Radioactive Decay —

_____

_____

_____

_____

Reactive —

_____

_____

_____

_____

Redox Reaction —

_____

_____

_____

_____

Refraction —

Light

Lens

_____

_____

_____

_____

Salt —

_____
_____
_____
_____

Solution —

_____
_____
_____
_____

States of Matter —

_____
_____
_____
_____

Sublimation —

_____
_____
_____
_____

Surface Tension —

_____

_____

_____

_____

Volume —

_____

_____

_____

_____

Chemistry for the Grammar Stage

Memory Work

Atoms and Molecules Unit

Atoms and Molecules

Atoms are the stuff that makes what we got,
Forming molecules found in your teapot.

Inside the atom are three little specks,
Subatomic particles kept in check.

At the center are neutrons and protons,
Spinning around in shells are electrons.

All three parts, balanced in equality,
Give the atom its own frivolity.

One or more atoms uniquely combine,
Creating a molecular design.

These molecules we can breathe, eat, and wear.
Meet them every day in water and air.

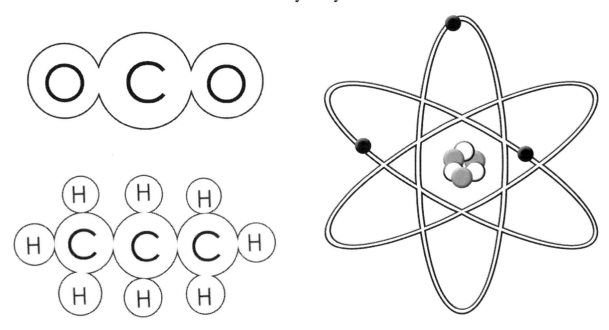

Periodic Table Unit

1
H
Hydrogen
1.008
3
Li
Lithium
6.941
11
Na
Sodium
22.99
19
K
Potassium
39.10
37
Rb
Rubidium
85.47
55
Cs
Cesium
132.9
87
Fr
Francium
[223]

<u>The Periodic Table</u> *(Author Unknown)*

Each element has a spot on the Periodic Table,
Whether metal or gas, radioactive or stable.
You can find out its number, its symbol, its weight,
And from its position, its physical state.

Elements lined up in columns and rows,
The reason for this order, as each chemist knows,
Is that atoms are made up of still smaller bits,
(Figuring this out tested scientists' wits!)

In the nucleus, protons and neutrons are found,
And a cloud of electrons is buzzing around.
First take one proton, put in its place;
Now you have hydrogen, the simplest case.

Add two neutrons and one more proton,
And suddenly, the hydrogen's gone!
Now you have helium, quite different stuff…
You get the picture; I've said enough.

These tiny particles: they're like building blocks
That make people and buildings, flowers and rocks.
They create all of the elements we find
In everyday things of every kind!

Physical Changes Unit

States of Matter

Three states of matter
Solid, liquid, gas
Molecules scatter
As heat enters mass

A solid is firm
Atoms locked in tight
No room found to squirm
We can take a bite

Liquid moves freely
Atoms flow and gush
Filling easily
Even helps you flush

A gas has no shape
Moves without control
It tries to escape
Out every hole

Chemical Changes Unit

Reactions

Atoms bump into each other in space
Bonding—connecting at a rapid pace
These compounds form in three main types of bonds
Different ways electrons correspond
In an ionic bond, one atom asks
The other gives electrons to the task
In a covalent bond the atoms share
Electrons joined in a happy pair
The metallic bond is a little strange
Electrons swirl in a constant exchange
This bonding happens in a reaction
Reactants to products—one cool action
As this tidy chemical change occurs
The mass stays the same, it only transfers
Exothermic reactions give off heat
Endothermic ones cool as atoms meet
Catalysts help by speeding up the pace
Redox is when electrons swap their place

$$HCl + NaOH \longrightarrow H_2O + NaCl$$

Mixtures Unit

<u>Mixtures, Solutions, Oh My!</u>

A mixture occurs when two things combine
Like in air, Kool-Aid, and a salty brine

A solid and liquid together mix
And form a solution—a mixture trick

One separates a mixture many ways
Filter, distill, evaporate—some stays

Through chromatography, people can see
Ink separate into colors with glee

Acids and Bases Unit

Acids and Bases

Acids dissolve in water to taste sour
Like the vinegar next to your flour

Bases break up into bitter compounds
Which can clean up stains left by coffee grounds

We measure their strength by the pH scale
Low for acids, high for base, tells the tale

But when we mix an acid and a base
Now, neutralization is what takes place

We see water and salt are left behind
A pH of 7 is what we find

Organic Chemistry Unit

<u>Organics</u>

Organic chem is the science of life
Carbon and hydrogen bond without strife

These compounds help keep our bodies
stable
But they can be made at the lab table

Alcohols have an OH group to boot
Esters make that sweet taste in gum or
fruit

Hydrocarbons are in gas and oil
Polymers create a long-chained coil

Chemistry for the Grammar Stage

Project Pictures

1		4			21	22	23	24	25	26	27	28	29	30

H — Hydrogen 1.008

Be 4 Beryllium 9.012

21	22	23	24	25	26	27	28	29	30
Sc	Ti	V	Cr	Mn	Fe	Co	Ni	Cu	Zn
Scandium	Titanium	Vanadium	Chromium	Manganese	Iron	Cobalt	Nickel	Copper	Zinc
44.96	47.87	50.94	52.00	54.94	55.85	58.93	58.69	63.55	65.39

39	40	41	42	43	44	45	46	47	48
Y	Zr	Nb	Mo	Tc	Ru	Rh	Pd	Ag	Cd
Yttrium	Zirconium	Niobium	Molybdenum	Technetium	Ruthenium	Rhodium	Palladium	Silver	Cadmium
88.91	91.22	92.91	95.94	98.91	101.1	102.9	106.4	107.9	112.4

*71	72	73	74	75	76	77	78	79	80
Lu	Hf	Ta	W	Re	Os	Ir	Pt	Au	Hg
Lutetium	Hafnium	Tantalum	Tungsten	Rhenium	Osmium	Iridium	Platinum	Gold	Mercury
175.0	178.5	181.0	183.9	186.2	190.2	192.2	195.1	197.0	200.6

3 Li Lithium 6.941
11 Na Sodium 22.99
19 K Potassium 39.10
37 Rb Rubidium 85.47
55 Cs Cesium 132.9
87 Fr Francium [223]

12 Mg Magnesium 24.31
20 Ca Calcium 40.08
38 Sr Strontium 87.62
56 Ba Barium 137.3
88 Ra Radium [226]

5	6	7	8
B	C	N	O
Boron	Carbon	Nitrogen	Oxygen
10.81	12.01	14.01	16.00
13	14	15	16
Al	Si	P	S
Aluminum	Silicon	Phosphorus	Sulfur
26.98	28.09	30.97	32.07
31	32	33	34
Ga	Ge	As	Se
Gallium	Germanium	Arsenic	Selenium
69.72	72.61	74.92	78.96
49	50	51	52
In	Sn	Sb	Te
Indium	Tin	Antimony	Tellurium
114.8	118.71	121.8	127.6
81	82	83	84
Tl	Pb	Bi	Po
Thallium	Lead	Bismuth	Polonium
204.4	207.2	209.0	[209]
113	114	115	116
Nh	Fl	Mc	Lv
Nihonium	Flerovium	Moscovium	Livermorium
[286]	[289]	[289]	[293]

Number	Symbol	Name	Mass
9	F	Fluorine	19.00
17	Cl	Chlorine	35.45
35	Br	Bromine	79.90
53	I	Iodine	126.9
85	At	Astatine	[210]
117	Ts	Tennessine	[294]

Number	Symbol	Name	Mass
2	He	Helium	4.003
10	Ne	Neon	20.18
18	Ar	Argon	39.95
36	Kr	Krypton	83.80
54	Xe	Xenon	131.3
86	Rn	Radon	[222]
118	Og	Oganesson	[294]

Number	Symbol	Name	Mass
89	Ac	Actinium	[227]
90	Th	Thorium	232.0
91	Pa	Protactinium	231.0
92	U	Uranium	238.0
93	Np	Neptunium	[237]
94	Pu	Plutonium	[244]
95	Am	Americium	[243]
96	Cm	Curium	[247]
97	Bk	Berkelium	[247]
98	Cf	Californium	[251]
99	Es	Einsteinium	[252]
100	Fm	Fermium	[257]
101	Md	Mendelevium	[258]
102	No	Nobelium	[259]

Number	Symbol	Name	Mass
57	La	Lanthanum	138.9
58	Ce	Cerium	140.1
59	Pr	Praseodymium	140.9
60	Nd	Neodymium	144.2
61	Pm	Promethium	[145]
62	Sm	Samarium	150.4
63	Eu	Europium	152.0
64	Gd	Gadolinium	157.3
65	Tb	Terbium	158.9
66	Dy	Dysprosium	162.5
67	Ho	Holmium	164.9
68	Er	Erbium	167.3
69	Tm	Thulium	168.9
70	Yb	Ytterbium	173.0

Chemistry for the Grammar Stage

Review Sheets

Atoms and Molecules Week 1 Review Sheet

1. Match the following subatomic particles with their charge.

   Proton   Neutral

   Electron   Negative

   Neutron   Positive

2. An atom has _____ and _____ in a mass at

   the center with _____ spinning around the outside.

3. **True or False:** An isotope is an atom that has a different number of neutrons.

4. What is the most interesting thing you learned this week?

   _____

   _____

   _____

   _____

   _____

Atoms and Molecules Week 2 Review Sheet

1. Fill in the blanks with the number of electrons found in the shell.

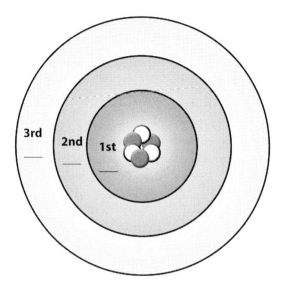

2. **True or False:** A molecule is always made up of only one element.

3. Polar molecules are (not charged / charged), while nonpolar molecules are (not charged / charged).

4. What is the most interesting thing you learned this week?

_____

_____

_____

_____

_____

_____

Atoms and Molecules Week 3 Review Sheet

1. Circle the two main gases that are found in air.

   oxygen   argon   nitrogen   chlorine

2. Oxygen is essential for _____.

   ice cream   life   rock formation

3. Animals take in (oxygen / carbon dioxide) and release (oxygen / carbon dioxide). Plants take in (oxygen / carbon dioxide) and release (oxygen / carbon dioxide).

5. What is the most interesting thing you learned this week?

   _____

   _____

   _____

   _____

   _____

   _____

Atoms and Molecules Week 4 Review Sheet

1. _____ is the most abundant compound on the earth.

2. Hard water has (more / less) dissolved minerals. Soft water has (more / less) dissolved minerals.

3. **True or False:** Surface tension is caused by the attraction of the molecules found in a liquid.

4. What is the most interesting thing you learned this week?

   _____

   _____

   _____

   _____

   _____

   _____

Periodic Table Week 1 Review Sheet

1. Fill in the blanks with atomic number, atomic mass, chemical name, and

   chemical symbol.

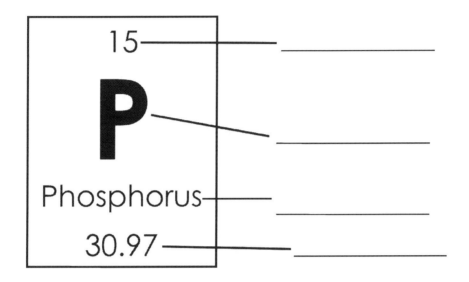

2. **True or False:** The periodic table was first designed by Dmitri Mendeleev.

3. **True or False:** An element is made up of multiple different atoms.

4. What is the most interesting thing you learned this week?

   _____

   _____

   _____

   _____

   _____

Periodic Table Week 2 Review Sheet

1. **True or False:** The alkali metals are a very reactive group.

2. Hydrogen exists as a _____ on Earth.

3. Circle all the characteristics of sodium.

        found in lots of common compounds   very reactive

        blue gas   light gray metal   very hard

4. What is the most interesting thing you learned this week?

_____

_____

_____

1
H
Hydrogen
1.008

_____

_____

_____

Periodic Table Week 3 Review Sheet

1. Circle all the characteristics of alkaline earth metals.

      soft metals   bond with alkali metals   react easily

2. **True or False:** Magnesium is a gas that burns with a bright purple-blue light.

3. Name two places that you can find calcium-containing compounds.

   _____

   _____

4. What is the most interesting thing you learned this week?

   _____

   _____

   _____

   _____

   _____

   _____

12
Mg
Magnesium
24.31

Periodic Table Week 4 Review Sheet

1. The transition metals are typically (good / poor) conductors of heat

    and electricity.

2. **True or False:** Iron is the most important metal on Earth.

3. Brass is an alloy of zinc and what transition metal?

          Iron   Copper   Chromium

4. What is the most interesting thing you learned this week?

    _____

    _____

    _____

```
 29
Cu
Copper
63.55
```

_____

_____

_____

Periodic Table Week 5 Review Sheet

1. **True or False:** Boron is the only element in the boron elements groups that is

   different than the rest.

2. **True or False:** Gallium and aluminum have the same melting points.

3. Aluminum is (a rare   /   an abundant   ) element on the Earth.

4. What is the most interesting thing you learned this week?

   _____

   _____

   _____

   _____

   _____

13

Al

Aluminum

26.98

Periodic Table Week 6 Review Sheet

1. The carbon elements group contains: (Circle all that apply.)

   metals   nonmetals   neither

2. Why is carbon so important to us?

   _____

   _____

   _____

3. **True or False:** Tin is NEVER used to form a metal alloy.

4. What is the most interesting thing you learned this week?

   _____

   _____

```
┌─────────────────┐
│       6         │
│                 │
│       C         │
│                 │
│     Carbon      │
│     12.01       │
└─────────────────┘
```
   _____

   _____

   _____

   _____

Periodic Table Week 7 Review Sheet

1. **True or False:** The nitrogen elements have a mish-mash collection of properties.

2. Nitrogen makes up almost _____ of the air on Earth.

    20 %   50 %   80 %

3. **True or False:** Arsenic has the properties of both metals and nonmetals.

4. What is the most interesting thing you learned this week?

_____

_____

_____

_____

_____

_____

_____

| 7 |
| N |
| Nitrogen |
| 14.01 |

Periodic Table Week 8 Review Sheet

1. The oxygen elements are (not important   /   important   ) to life and

   industry.

2. Why is oxygen so important to us?

   _____

   _____

   _____

3. **True or False:** Pure sulfur is a pale yellow solid and it has compounds that

   smell like rotten eggs.

4. What is the most interesting thing you learned this week?

8
O
Oxygen
16.00

_____

_____

_____

_____

_____

_____

Periodic Table Week 9 Review Sheet

1. **True or False:** Fluorine is the least reactive element in the halogen group.

2. Halogens stands for _____ because they form

   _____ easily with metals.

3. **True or False:** Iodine is important to the human diet.

4. What is the most interesting thing you learned this week?

   _____

   _____

   _____

   _____

   _____

| 53 |
| I |
| Iodine |
| 126.9 |

1. The noble gases are the (most   /   least   ) reactive elements in the periodic

   table.

2. **True or False:** Helium is heavier than air.

3. Krypton is often used in _____.

   food   lights   ladders

4. What is the most interesting thing you learned this week?

   _____

   _____

   _____

10	_____
Ne	_____
Neon	_____
20.18	_____

Periodic Table Week 11 Review Sheet

1. **True or False:** Many of the elements in lanthanide group are naturally occurring.

2. Lanthanum is often used in _____.

         steel   good lens   bookcases

3. Neodymium is (not   /   very   ) magnetic.

4. What is the most interesting thing you learned this week?

   _____

   _____

   _____

   _____

   _____

   _____

   _____

| 57 |
| La |
| Lanthanum |
| 138.9 |

Periodic Table Week 12 Review Sheet

1. **True or False:** Many of the elements in the actinide group are radioactive.

2. In radioactive decay, an atom loses particles until it becomes a more

   _____.

3. Uranium is often used in _____.

   generating power   purifying water   cleaning up spills

4. What is the most interesting thing you learned this week?

   _____

   _____

   _____

   _____

   _____

   _____

   _____

   _____

| 92 |
| U |
| Uranium |
| 238.0 |

Physical Changes Week 1 Review Sheet

1. Match the state of matter.

   Solid _____   A. Has no fixed shape or volume.

   Liquid _____   B. Has a fixed shape and volume.

   Gas _____   C. Has a fixed volume, but not a fixed shape.

2. **True or False:** Volume is the amount of space occupied by matter.

3. **True or False:** The molecules in a gas have less energy than the molecules in a solid.

4. What is the most interesting thing you learned this week?

   _____

   _____

   _____

   _____

   _____

   _____

Physical Changes Week 2 Review Sheet

1. When a solid _____, it turns into a liquid.

   When a liquid _____, it turns into a gas.

       melts   boils   condenses

2. When a liquid _____, it turns into a solid.

   When a liquid _____, it turns into a gas.

       condenses   freezes   evaporates

3. What is the most interesting thing you learned this week?

   _____

   _____

   _____

                          _____

                          _____

                          _____

Solid

Liquid

Gas

Physical Changes Week 3 Review Sheet

1. Liquids can change _____, but the _____

remains the same.

volume   shape   color

2. **True or False:** The cooler a liquid gets, the quicker it evaporates.

3. **True or False:** Surface tension is the result of the molecules in a liquid being

attracted to each other.

4. What is the most interesting thing you learned this week?

_____

_____

_____

_____

_____

_____

Physical Changes Week 4 Review Sheet

1. **True or False:** Brownian motion is the random motion of molecules within a liquid or gas.

2. In diffusion, molecules move from an area of (high / low) concentration to an area of (high / low) concentration.

3. _____ is the push that gas molecules exert on a container.

    volume   pressure   temperature

4. What is the most interesting thing you learned this week?

    _____

    _____

    _____

                        _____

                        _____

                        _____

Chemical Changes Week 1 Review Sheet

1. In _____ bonding an electron is gained or lost.

   ionic   covalent   metallic

2. In _____ bonding electrons are free to travel within a lattice.

   ionic   covalent   metallic

3. In _____ bonding an electron is shared between two atoms.

   ionic   covalent   metallic

4. What is the most interesting thing you learned this week?

   _____

   _____

   _____

   _____

   _____

   _____

Chemical Changes Week 2 Review Sheet

1. A chemical reaction begins with (reactants   /   products   ) and ends with

    (reactants   /   products   ).

2. The Law of Conservation of Mass says that amount of matter in a chemical

    reaction_____.

    increases   stays the same   decreases

3. **True or False:** A mole is the unit that chemists use to measure substances.

4. What is the most interesting thing you learned this week?

    _____

    _____

    _____

    _____

    _____

    _____

Chemical Changes Week 3 Review Sheet

1. A reaction that produces heat is called an _____ reaction. A reaction that takes in heat is called an _____ reaction.

      endothermic   activated   exothermic

2. **True or False:** A catalyst can only slow down a reaction.

3. A catalyst that speeds up a reaction in a living thing is called an _____.

      quickinator   enzyme   protein

4. What is the most interesting thing you learned this week?

   _____

   _____

   _____

   _____

   _____

   _____

Chemical Changes Week 4 Review Sheet

1. **True or False:** An oxidation or reduction, a.k.a. redox, reaction involves the transfer of electrons.

2. Combustion is an example of a(n) _____ reaction.

   oxidation   reduction

3. Photosynthesis is an example of a(n) _____ reaction.

   oxidation   reduction

4. What is the most interesting thing you learned this week?

   _____

   _____

   _____

   _____

   _____

   _____

Mixtures Week 1 Review Sheet

1. **True or False:** A mixture contains a combination a two or more elements.

2. A solution is formed when a _____ is dissolved in a liquid.

    gas   liquid   solid

3. When two liquids mix easily, they are called (immiscible / miscible).

    When two liquids do not mix easily, they are called (immiscible / miscible).

4. What is the most interesting thing you learned this week?

    _____

    _____

    _____

    _____

    _____

    _____

Mixtures Week 2 Review Sheet

1. Filtration is a method of separating _____.

   liquids from gases   solids from liquids   solids from gases

2. **True or False:** You can not use chromatography to determine what colors are in an ink pen.

3. Distillation is a method of separating two or more _____.

   solids   liquids   gases

4. What is the most interesting thing you learned this week?

   _____

   _____

   _____

   _____

   _____

   _____

Mixtures Week 3 Review Sheet

1. Crystals form as a solution _____.

        Cools off   Heats up

2. **True or False:** A crystal is a solid with a definite geometric shape.

3. **True or False:** Crystals only have rounded edges and surfaces.

4. What is the most interesting thing you learned this week?

   _____

   _____

   _____

   _____

   _____

Mixtures Week 4 Review Sheet

1. What have you learned about Louis Pasteur this week?

_____

_____

_____

_____

_____

_____

_____

_____

Acids and Bases Week 1 Review Sheet

1. **True or False:** An acid dissolves in water and can taste sour.

2. Some common acids are _____.

       vinegar   water   ammonia   lemon juice

2. **True or False:** An base dissolves in water and can taste sour.

3. Some common acids are _____.

       water   baking soda   ammonia   lemon juice

4. What is the most interesting thing you learned this week?

_____

_____

_____

_____

_____

_____

Acids and Bases Week 2 Review Sheet

1. pH stands for _____.

   potential of hydrology   power of hydrogren

2. Label the following pH's with what they represent - acid, base, or neutral.

   pH 2 _____

   pH 7 _____

   pH 10 _____

3. **True or False:** An indicator is a substance that changes color in the presence of an acid or a base.

4. What is the most interesting thing you learned this week?

Neutral

Base   Acid

_____

_____

_____

_____

_____

Acids and Bases Week 3 Review Sheet

1. When you mix an acid and a base, you get _____ and

   a _____.

2. **True or False:** A salt is formed when you mix an acid and a base.

3. A salt dissolves in water to form _____.

   bases   ions   acids

4. What is the most interesting thing you learned this week?

   _____

   _____

   _____

   _____

   _____

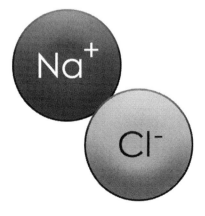

Acids and Bases Week 4 Review Sheet

1. What have you learned about Marie Curie this week?

    _____

    _____

    _____

    _____

    _____

    _____

    _____

    _____

Organic Chemistry Week 1 Review Sheet

1. All organic compounds have _____.

2. **True or False:** Organic acids behave the same as other acids.

3. A _____ is a substance that allows water to remove dirt.

        acids   detergents   esters

4. What is the most interesting thing you learned this week?

_____

_____

_____

_____

_____

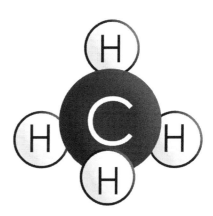

Organic Chemistry Week 2 Review Sheet

1. Circle the elements below that are found in alcohols.

   Carbon   Hydrogen   Iron   Oxygen

2. **True or False:** Fermentation is a chemical reaction that produces an organic acid.

3. Esters are responsible for the _____ in flowers, fruit, and perfume.

   touch   taste   smell

4. What is the most interesting thing you learned this week?

   _____

   _____

   _____

   _____

   _____

   _____

Organic Chemistry Week 3 Review Sheet

1. **True or False:** Crude oil can be separated through distillation to make a lot of useful hydrocarbon compounds.

2. Circle the following chemicals that are hydrocarbons.

   gas   oil   kerosene

   candle wax   lubricants

3. Crude oil is separated by a process called _____.

   pulling   fractional distillation   blast separation

4. What is the most interesting thing you learned this week?

   _____

   _____

   _____

   _____

   _____

   _____

Organic Chemistry Week 4 Review Sheet

1. Polymers are made up of _____ chains of molecules.

    short   long

2. **True or False:** Polymerization is the process of joining up molecules to make

   polymers.

3. Synthetic polymers and plastics are made by _____.

    man   nature

4. What is the most interesting thing you learned this week?

   _____

   _____

   _____

                                  _____

                                  _____

                                  _____

Made in the USA
Las Vegas, NV
16 August 2024

93902982R00094